age 3-5

C000061877

get ready for reading

Written by Nicola Morgan MA
an experienced teacher with a diploma in literacy teaching
Illustrations by John Haslam

Tips for happy learning

★ Create success by working at your child's pace and always giving tasks
which he/she can do. Asking your child to do something which is too difficult
will discourage him/her.

★ Give lots of praise for trying hard and reward your child with the gold stars
and sticker badges.

★ Always do too little rather than too much — stop BEFORE he/she wants to.

★ Make sure your work sessions are happy and comfortable — don't work when you
or your child are tired or hungry.

★ Read stories to your child as often as you can.

HAPPY LEARNERS LEARN FAST

Series editor: Nina Filipek
Series designer: Paul Dronsfield MCSD
Designer: Gail M Rose

get
ready
for
reading

About this book

This book develops the visual skills which your child needs before learning to read real words. First it asks him/her to look closely at shapes and pictures. Later, real letters are introduced — but we are still looking at visual details in the shapes rather than talking about the sounds.

Children know nothing about the 'squiggles' (printed words) on the page.
They look at the pictures and may not notice anything else. Looking at pictures is important but they also need to learn to focus on print, and to notice important differences between the squiggles, long before they can know what the print means. That is what this book aims to do.

You may not be a professional teacher but you are the best teacher for your child. Here are some tips for using this book with your child:

Sit NEXT TO your child, rather than opposite (otherwise he/she will see you reading and writing 'backwards').
★
Teach your child how to hold the pencil correctly
(consider buying a pencil grip).
★
Where instructions are directed at the child, read them aloud, pointing to the words as you do.
★
Make sure he/she understands what to do.
Repeat the instructions if necessary.
★
The exercises increase in difficulty, so try to work through the pages in order.
★
These workbooks work best if used in conjunction with practical activities and story-telling. Lots of practical activities are suggested throughout the book.

Special note for left-handers:

If you or your child is left-handed, special care must be taken. If you are left-handed but your child is not, use your right hand when showing him/her how to write or draw shapes and when following print with your finger. If your child is left-handed but you are not, use your left hand. If your child seems to be ambidextrous, try to discover which is his/her better hand and encourage him/her to use that one consistently.

Hello! I'm Curly Cat.

I'm going to help you learn to read. When we read we look at the words – not the pictures. Point to some words on this page.

Words/ pictures

Can you put a circle round just the words?

hat

flower

cat

house

tree

balloon

Learning point: it seems so obvious to us that words and pictures are different, but children need to learn this.

Activity: next time you go shopping, point out the names of shops or anything else with words on – not expecting your child to remember but just so he/she learns that there is a message in print.

Draw a circle round the words again.
What do you think the words say?

Words/
pictures

house   sun   balloon   tree

hat   kite   mug   star

One special word is your name. Ask a grown-up to write it here:

Can you draw a picture of yourself?

You have
learnt about
words.

You are doing such good work.
Find the badge which says 'I know about words'.

4

Nice to see you again.

Use your eyes carefully to find shapes which are the same and join them with a line.

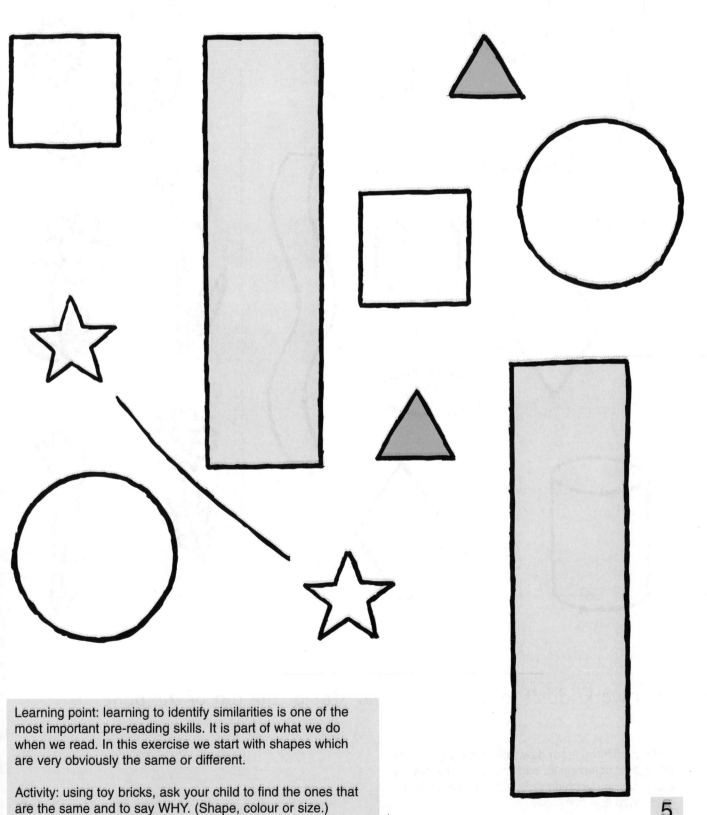

Learning point: learning to identify similarities is one of the most important pre-reading skills. It is part of what we do when we read. In this exercise we start with shapes which are very obviously the same or different.

Activity: using toy bricks, ask your child to find the ones that are the same and to say WHY. (Shape, colour or size.)

Let's do some more matching.

Good work: don't forget to put your star at the top of the page.

Activity: children learn new skills more easily if you
use actual objects first, such as toy bricks, cutlery
etc. Practise matching skills with games such as
lotto, snap and dominoes.

I need some help. These gloves are muddled up. Can you find the ones which match and join them with a line?

Learning point: here we are asking your child to look more closely than before.

Activity: how about asking your child to help you sort out all the socks in the washing?

Find the badge which says 'I can match patterns'.

Can you use your eyes really carefully here?
Join the snowflakes which are the same.

Can you draw some snowflakes of your own?

Learning point: reward is a vital part of learning. A child
who does not receive enough encouragement can be put
off learning altogether. The best reward of all is praise,
but a physical sign, such as a sticker, means a lot to your
child. Praise your child for trying, even if he/she needed help.

8

You will find these easy.
Look at the first one in each line
then circle one that's the same.

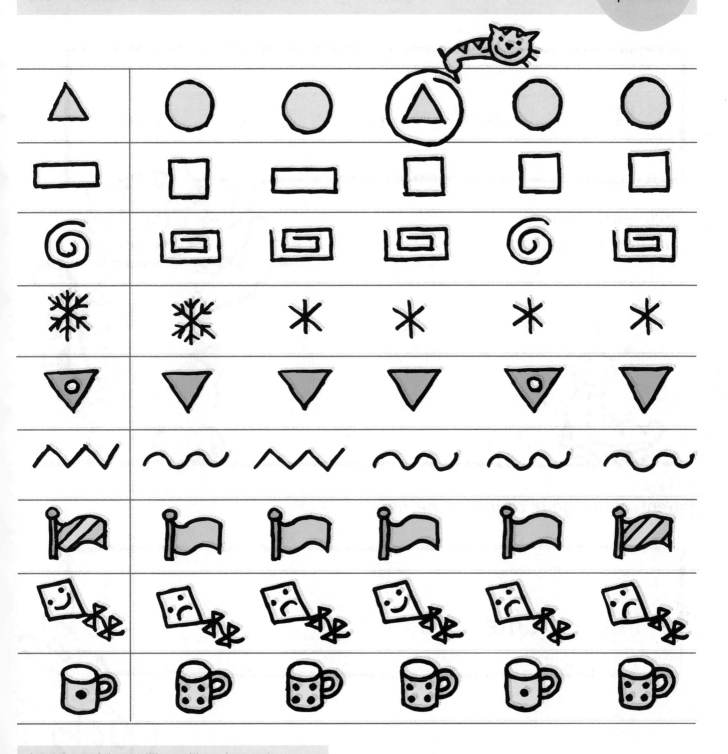

Learning point: repetition, with an increasing
feeling of success, is the key to this page.
Some children lack confidence and ask for help
when they don't really need it. There is nothing
wrong with asking for help but gently encourage
your child to do it on his/her own. Then, pile on the
praise.

Find the badge which says
'clever me'.

Words have spaces to keep them apart.
Can you read these words?

My   name   is   Curly   Cat.

Circle each word.
Can you count them?

Parent: write your child's name here.

My   name   is

Circle and count each word. Which is the biggest word?

Learning point: children can't learn to read until they can see words as separate units. This takes practice.

Tip: when reading to your child, point to individual words. Sometimes ask your child to count the words in a sentence.

10

Words can only go one way. If they go the wrong way we can't read them.

 This star shows which side words start. Start at the star.

Your name must go the right way, too.
Parent: write your child's name here.

Let's practise going the right way.
Follow these paths with your finger first.
Then do it with a pencil.

Learning point: direction of print needs to be reinforced from an early age. Children may take a long time to get the hang of it. It is even more important for left-handers or for a child who may find learning to read difficult for any reason. You could put a star on your child's left hand, or make a star card (see next page).

11

Let's practise drawing lines that go the same way as words.
Help these animals find their food.

Activity: make a star card. Take a piece of card bigger than
this open workbook. With the card horizontal, put a picture in
the top right corner (so that your child can see which way up
the card goes). In the top left corner, put a large star.
When your child is doing any pencil work, the card should
be underneath the book or paper, with the star showing in
the top left corner. Reinforce the motto: start at the star.

Find the badge which
says 'clever cat'.

12

Let's practise some more.
Help these animals find their homes.

Great work! You did that so well.
Now you can find the badge which says:
'I know which way words go'.

Are you having fun?

You are learning such a lot.

13

This page lets you match pictures AND draw a line the right way.

Join each picture on the left with the same one on the right.

Good work!

Lovely work. Well done!

These pictures are like stories.
On the left are things which happen first.
Join each one across to the thing which happens next.

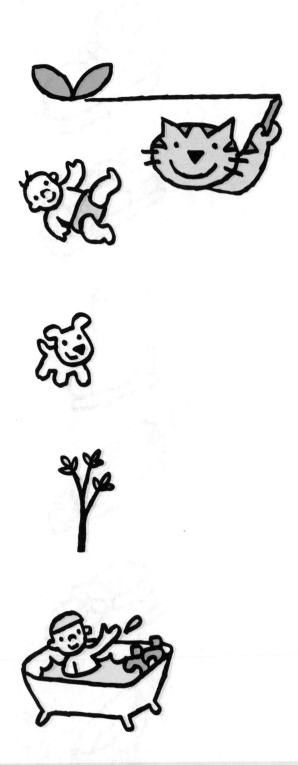

Learning point: the sequence of a story is like the direction of
print – it has only one order. Talk about this exercise and ask
your child about other sequences during the day: eg which
comes first, breakfast or lunch?

16

Now let's look at real letters.
Letters are the little bits that make words.
Each one has a special shape.

Look at these letter shapes and join the ones that are the same.

a   s   t

p   t   s   n

a   p   n

Well done you!
Find the badge which says 'I like looking for letters'.

Learning point: this is just like a shape-matching exercise.
At this stage your child does not need to know what sound
the letters make. At first, we are using only letters which have
obvious similarities and differences, avoiding the
confusing ones like b/d, p/q, n/u.

You did some work with real letters.

17

Here are some more letters to match.
Look carefully at the shapes.

And here are some more:

Wonderful work! Don't forget to get your star.

Let's do one more page like that.
Are you holding your pencil properly?

n   e   h

s   o   n   p

e   p

h   o   s

Here are the letters which make the word **cat**.

Look at the letters below and put a circle round the ones which you can see in cat.

m   c   s   a   p   i   t

Find the badge which says
'I can match letters'.

19

Here are some more letters.
Join each one on the left to the same one on the right.
Put a star on the side of the page where you start.

⭐ a   s

i   a

s   p

e   h

p   i

h   e

Well done!

n   k

l   r

k   n

t   w

r   l

w   t

Activity: find two examples of one well-known shop name (for example on a carrier bag or own-brand food packet). Cut one of the examples into separate letters. Ask your child to lay the cut-up letters in the right order underneath the whole word. This helps practise letter-matching as well as direction of print.

Good work!

You'll need to look extra carefully at these letters.
Some of them look nearly the same.

a   o   e

i   c

o   e   i

c   a

Learning point: these letters are slightly harder for your child to match because they all have a similar shape. From now on, your child will need to look more closely at differences between letters.

Find the badge which says 'I did brilliant work'.

Do the same here. Look very carefully.

d   a   d

o   h   n   v

v   o   h   w

a   n   w

I did brilliant work.

Activity: make a double set of alphabet cards (or use letters from a game such as Scrabble). Select just the ones we have been using so far and ask your child to find pairs.
Remember: children often need practice with physical things before being confident on paper.

Note: so far, we have not combined letters like b/d, p/q, n/u, because children will need quite advanced matching skills. In preparation, the next few pages ask the child to notice differences in direction, using pictures and shapes first.

Here's something new.
Some of these things point different ways.

Look at the picture on the left (the star side).
Then look along the line and circle one that points the same way.
They must be the same way up, too.

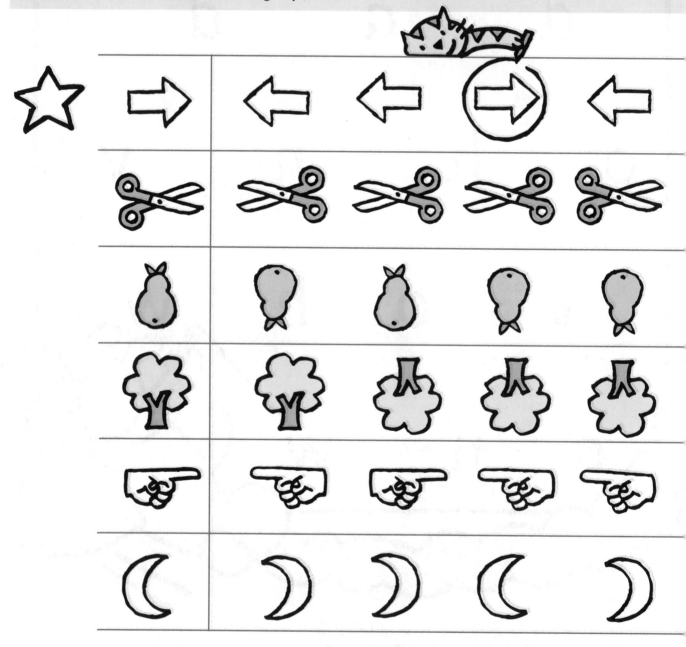

Activity: reinforce this idea with real objects.
Find two examples of some of these: cutlery, toy
animals, pencils, etc. Lay one in a particular
direction and ask your child to put the other one
in the same direction.

Let's do some more like that.

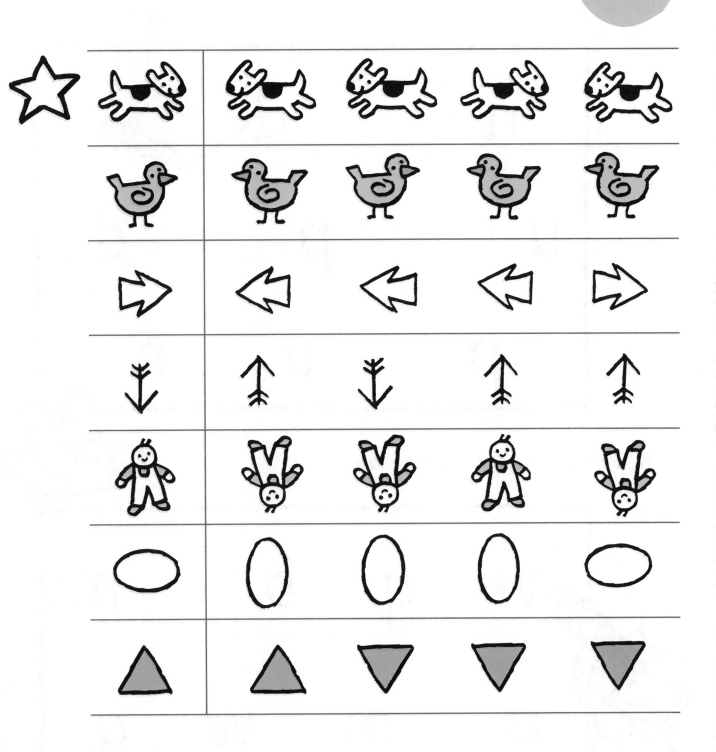

Learning point: the next pages work on letters which are mirror images of other letters, so your child needs to be confident about this page and the previous one. Don't worry if your child isn't quite ready for this. Practise with real objects and give plenty of help.

Look very carefully at these tricky letters.
Join the same ones with a line.
Remember, they have to point the same way.

n   d

u   p   d

p   u   n

Well done you! Now try some more.

w   q   b   m

b   m   w   q

That was good.

Let's do some more like that.

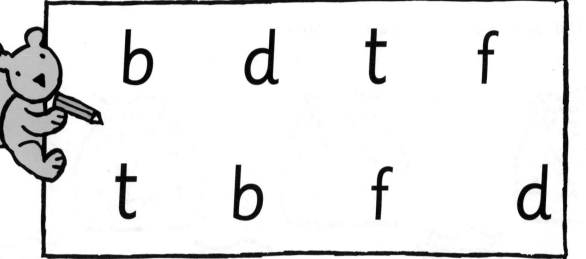

| b | d | t | f |
| t | b | f | d |

And one more time . . .

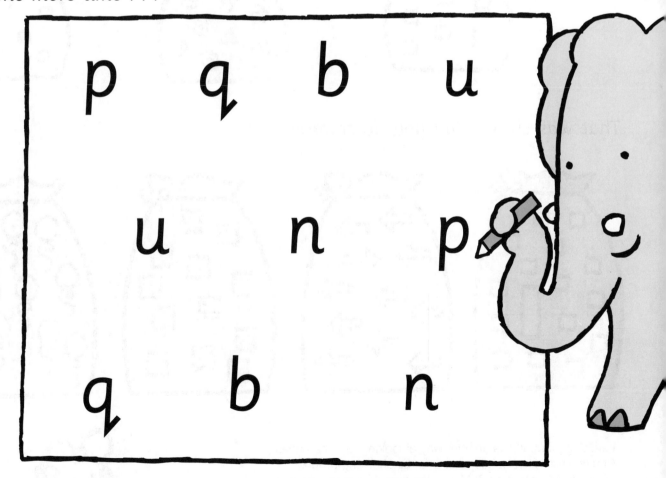

p	q	b	u
u		n	p
q	b		n

You have won another badge.
Find the one which says 'brilliant at matching letters'.

27

Here's something new.
Do you know about odd one out?
The odd one out is the one that's different from all the others.

Circle the odd one out inside each sack.

That was clever. Can you do some more?

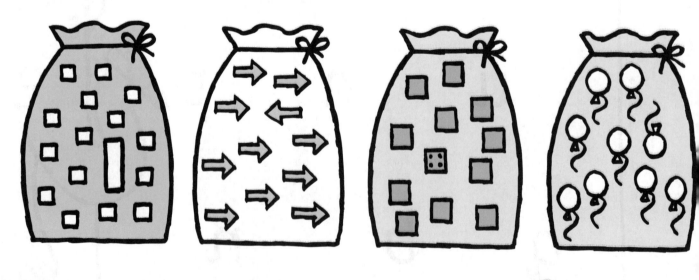

Learning point: this is another way of looking for differences.
Practise with physical objects. Start by choosing groups
where all but one are EXACTLY the same (eg four identical
blue bricks and one yellow one). Gradually move to groups
where the 'linked' ones are not quite identical (eg three
assorted cups and one spoon).